A car came to the house
The children ran to see.
'It's Gran,' said Kipper.

1

'Come in,' said Mum.
'Come in,' said Dad.

The children helped.
They took Gran's things.
'What a lot of things!' said Kipper.

The children liked Gran and
Gran liked the children.

'Come and see my toys,' said Kipper.
'Come and see my room,' said Biff.
'Come and play,' said Chip.

5

Gran played with the children.
They played inside.
'Oh no!' said Mum.

They went outside and
played football.
'Oh no!' said Dad.

Gran took the children out.
They went in Gran's old car.
Wilf and Wilma went too.

'What an old car!' said Wilf.
'It's a good car,' said Gran.

Gran took them to the fun park.
'This looks fun,' said Gran.
'Come on, everyone.'

The children began to run.
They wanted to go on everything.
'Come on, Gran,' they called.

'Look at this,' said Kipper.
'It's a castle.
It's called Jumping Castle.'

The children went on
the jumping castle.
'This is fun,' called Wilma.

The children jumped and jumped, and
bounced and bounced.
'Come on, Gran,' they called.

Gran went on the castle.
She jumped and bounced.
'Good old Gran,' called the children.

Gran made a hole in the castle.
'Oh no!' said the children.
The castle began to go down.

A man ran up.

He was cross with Gran.

'Look at my castle,' he yelled.

'Go home,' yelled the man, 'and
don't come back.'
Gran took the children home.

Biff told Mum about the castle.
Mum was cross with Gran.
Gran was sad.

Gran was in Chip's room.
She looked at the magic key.
The key was glowing.

Gran picked up the key and
 ran into Biff's room.
'Look at this,' she said.

'Oh no!' said Kipper.
'It's the magic.
The magic is working.'

The magic took them to
a new adventure.